A B C D E F G H I J K L M
N O P Q R S T U

Meet big **O** and little **o**.

Trace each letter with your finger and say its name.

O is for

octopus

O is also for

ox

ostrich

otter

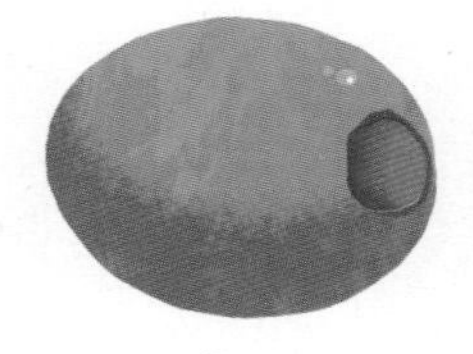

olive

This **o**ctopus is **O**scar.
Oscar lives in the water.

Can **O**scar play with an **o**x
and an **o**strich? No.
Those animals live **o**n land.

Can **O**scar play with an **o**tter? Yes. An **o**tter lives in water just like an **o**ctopus.

Oscar and the **o**tter juggle **o**lives!

They draw **o**ctagons and **o**dd creatures!

Oscar and the **o**tter play **o**ften and it's always a lot **o**f fun.